GREATER LONDON CEMETERIES AND CREMATORIA

compi
Patricia S

revised by
Cliff Webb M.A. F.S.G.

SOCIETY OF GENEALOGISTS ENTERPRISES LTD

Published by
Society of Genealogists Enterprises Limited
14 Charterhouse Buildings
Goswell Road
London EC1M 7BA

First Edition, 1982
Second Edition, 1985
Third Edition, 1994
Fourth Edition, 1996
Fifth Edition, 1997
Sixth Edition, 1999
Seventh Edition, 2005
Reprinted 2007, 2009

ISBN 10: 1 85951 704 8
ISBN 13: 978 1 85951 704 8

CONTENTS

THE LONDON BOROUGHS

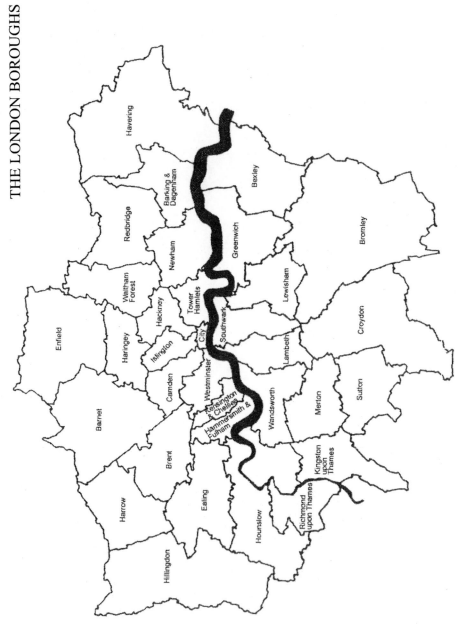

PREFACE TO 2005 EDITION

In this revised edition, the opportunity has been taken to give website addresses for cemeteries wherever these appear useful. Relatively few cemeteries' records have been published or are searchable online, but where they are this most welcome development has been noted with the appropriate publisher/website address. Many of the larger cemeteries are attracting groups of friends, again website addresses have been provided. As everyone will appreciate, websites are transient creatures, and some site addresses are likely to become quickly out of date, and others will appear. They should always be looked for.

INTRODUCTION

Locating the burial place of a nineteenth-century resident of the Greater London area is far from an easy task, and the same applies to those who died in the last century.

While many burials continued in the local churchyards of the outer London parishes, burials in the inner London churchyards or burial grounds were discontinued at various dates in the 1850s and no parish burial registers were maintained thereafter. Subsequently most burials for inner London took place further away, at non-denominational cemeteries established by either commercial companies or local government bodies.

Exceptions were those established by the Jewish community and the Roman Catholic Church.

THE SEARCH

Some of the following guidelines may prove of value:

1. The deceased of certain areas of London have tended to predominate in certain cemeteries:
   residents of North London in Highgate Cemetery
   residents of East London in Tower Hamlets, Victoria Park and Brookwood Cemeteries
   residents of South London in Norwood and Nunhead Cemeteries
   residents of West London in Kensal Green Cemetery.

2. Economic status could affect the location of burial. Brookwood Cemetery and others competed to undertake contracts tendered each year by several London boroughs for the burial of their poor. Although out of the Greater London Council area, Brookwood probably buried half of East London and to facilitate this Waterloo Station had a special casket-loading platform.

3. The St Marylebone Cemetery catered for the affluent middle classes of Marylebone, Highgate and Hampstead, with a high proportion also in the professional and military occupations.

4. Certain parishes bought parcels of newly established cemeteries: St George Hanover Square at Hanwell, and St Anne Soho, St Margaret and St John Westminster at Brookwood. At Norwood an area was reserved for the brotherhood of the Greek community in London.

5. Foremost amongst the burial grounds devoted especially to Dissenters was Bunhill Fields and afterwards Abney Park Cemetery. For those who were Quakers it would be advisable to undertake the search at the library of the Religious Society of Friends, Friends House, Euston Road, London NW1 2BJ (020 7663 1001; E-mail: library@quaker.org.uk; Website: http://www.quaker.org.uk/library/).

6. Just as the names of the registration districts used by the General Register Office keep changing so do those of the cemeteries. As ownership changes, so do some of the names, although obviously not the location; hence if encountering difficulty it is wise to check for similarity of address.

BEFORE CONTACTING A REPOSITORY

Not all registers contain indexes and in some cases where they exist they are for owners of grave plots rather than individuals interred there. Therefore it is strongly recommended that the appropriate date of death be ascertained prior to making any contact with a source listed below. Where it has been indicated that a member of the public MAY NOT undertake the search, we have been requested to provide:

the name of the deceased
the approximate date of death
the reason the information is being requested.

Since some repositories charge a fee, do not be surprised if that proves to be the case with the one you approach.

Where it has been indicated that a member of the public may undertake the search, it is recommended that an appointment be requested a minimum of 24 hours in advance. Many of these places are primarily engaged in the planning of present-day funerals which must obviously take precedence.

For those interested in the history, architectural features, identity of the well-known buried there, or the current physical conditions of a particular cemetery, several books may be consulted. The following provide an excellent introduction:

The London burial grounds, Mrs. Basil Holmes (1896)
Wate's book of London churchyards, Harvey Hackman (1981)
Permanent Londoner: an illustrated guide to the cemeteries of London, J. Culbertson & T. Randall, 1991)

London cemeteries, Hugh Meller (1981, 3rd ed., 1994)
'The development of London's cemeteries' (J.M. Clarke, *Genealogists' Magazine*, Vol. 26, 1998, pp.9-13)

Photographs of many London Cemeteries are available online at
www.londoncemeteries.co.uk/

ACKNOWLEDGEMENTS

The compiler and reviser are indebted to some known and many more unknown individuals all of whom kindly and patiently replied to numerous queries. Graham Bird, Meryl Catty, Susan Lumas, Peter Searle and Elizabeth Silverthorne also lent help in collecting updated details. George Rigal and Charles Tucker supplied information for the Jewish section. Despite their co-operation there may still be inaccuracies or omissions; information concerning these will be gratefully received. The cover illustration is based on a photograph in West Norwood Cemetery by Paul Blake.

GEOGRAPHICAL DISTRIBUTION

The Tables are designed to show the geographical area (N-E-S-W-) of all, except the Jewish, burial places considered to be 'local'; i.e. either owned by the governmental unit or physically located in the said area if commercially sponsored.

Reading from left to right, the second column provides the name of the pre-1965 authority formerly in the London County Council (L.C.C.), the old county of Middlesex, or the counties of Essex, Hertfordshire, Kent and Surrey. Column three indicates the 1984 name of the London Borough covering that same area under the Greater London Council and which boroughs now operate independently. The final column indicates the 'local' cemetery or crematorium and in brackets the date of its first register.

area	pre-1965 authority	present authority	local cemeteries/crematoria
	City of London Corporation	City of London Corporation	Bunhill Fields Burial Ground (1713) City of London Cemetery Little Ilford (1856) City of London Crematorium (1905)
N	Finsbury Islington (L.C.C.)	Islington	Spa Fields (1778) Islington Cemetery High Road (1854) Islington Cemetery Cockfosters Road (1960) Islington Crematorium (1937)

area	pre-1965 authority	present authority	local cemeteries/crematoria
N	Hornsey Tottenham Wood Green (Middlesex)	Haringey	Tottenham Cemetery (1856)
N	Edmonton Enfield Southgate (Middlesex)	Enfield	Edmonton Cemetery (1884) Old Southgate Cemetery (c.1880) Enfield Crematorium (1938) Enfield Lawn Cemetery (1961) Hertford Road Cemetery (1881) Lavender Hill Cemetery (1872) Tottenham Park Cemetery (1912)
NE	Hackney Shoreditch Stoke Newington (L.C.C.)	Hackney	Abney Park Cemetery (Nonconformist; 1840) St Thomas Square Cemetery (1837) Victoria Park Cemetery (1853)
NE	Chingford Leyton Walthamstow (Essex)	Waltham Forest	Chingford Mount Cemetery (1886) Walthamstow Cemetery (1872)
NE	Part of Chigwell Ilford Wanstead & Woodford (Essex)	Redbridge	Barkingside Cemetery (1923) Barkingside Garden of Rest (1953) Buckingham Road Cemetery (1881) Roding Lane Cemetery (1940)
E	Bethnal Green Poplar Stepney (L.C.C.)	Tower Hamlets	Tower Hamlets Cemetery (1841) (see **Introduction** re Brookwood) Gibraltar Row Burial Ground (1793)
E	East Ham West Ham (Essex)	Newham	East London Cemetery (1874) Manor Park Cemetery (1874) West Ham Cemetery (1854) Woodgrange Park Cemetery (1889)
E	Barking[1] Dagenham (Essex)	Barking	Barkingside Cemetery (1923) Chadwell Heath Cemetery (1934) Eastbrookend Cemetery (1914) Rippleside Cemetery (1886)

1. A very small area formerly in Barking but west of Barking Creek is now in Newham.

area	pre-1965 authority	present authority	local cemeteries/crematoria
E	Hornchurch Romford (Essex)	Havering	Hornchurch Cemetery (1932) Rainham Cemetery (1902) Romford Cemetery (1871) South Essex Crematorium (1950) Upminster Cemetery (1902)
SE	Bermondsey Camberwell Southwark (L.C.C.)	Southwark	Camberwell Cemetery (1856) Camberwell New Cemetery (1927) Honor Oak Crematorium (1939) Nunhead Cemetery (1840)
SE	Greenwich Woolwich^2 (L.C.C.)	Greenwich	Charlton Cemetery (1864) Eltham Cemetery (1935) Greenwich Cemetery (1856) Plumstead Cemetery (1890) Royal Hospital Cemetery (Navy; 1848) Woolwich Cemeteries (1856, 1885)
SE	Deptford Lewisham (L.C.C.)	Lewisham	Brockley Cemetery (1858) Grove Park Cemetery (1935) Hither Green Cemetery (1873) Ladywell Cemetery (1858) Lewisham Crematorium (1956)
SE	Bexley Crayford Part of Chisle-hurst & Sidcup Erith (Kent)	Bexley	Bexleyheath Cemetery (1879) Erith Cemetery (1894) Sidcup Cemetery (1912)
SE	Beckenham Bromley Part of Chisle-hurst & Sidcup Orpington Penge* (Kent)	Bromley	Beckenham Cemetery (1876) Beckenham Crematorium (1956) Biggin Hill Cemetery (1937) Bromley Hill Cemetery (1907) Chislehurst Cemetery (1912) London Road Cemetery (1877) Plaistow Cemetery (1892) St Luke's Cemetery (1894) St Mary Cray Cemetery (1884)
S	Croydon Coulsdon & Purley (Surrey)	Croydon	Croydon Cemetery (1897) Croydon Crematorium (1937) Greenlawn Memorial Park (1940) Queen's Road Cemetery (1861)

2. Two very small enclaves north of the Thames, formerly in Woolwich, are now in Newham.

area	pre-1965 authority	present authority	local cemeteries/crematoria
SW	Lambeth Part of Wandsworth (i.e.Clapham & Streatham) (L.C.C.)	Lambeth	Lambeth Cemetery (1854) Streatham Cemetery (1893) West Norwood Cemetery (1837) West Norwood Crematorium (1915)
SW	Battersea Wandsworth (except for Clapham & Streatham area) (L.C.C.)	Wandsworth	Battersea St Mary's Cemetery (1860) Putney Lower Common Cemetery (1855) Putney Vale Cemetery (1891) Wandsworth Cemetery (1878) Morden Cemetery (Battersea New Cemetery (1892) North East Surrey Crematorium (1958)
SW	Merton & Morden Mitcham Wimbledon (Surrey)	Merton	Merton & Sutton Joint Cemetery (1947) Mitcham Cemetery, Church Road (1883) Mitcham Cemetery, London Road (1929) South London Crematorium (1936) Streatham Cemetery (1893) Streatham Park Cemetery (1911) Wimbledon Cemetery (1876)
SW	Beddington & Wallington Carshalton Sutton & Cheam (Surrey)	Sutton	Bandon Hill Cemetery (1899) Cuddington Cemetery (1902) Sutton Cemetery (1889)
SW	Barnes Richmond-upon-Thames (Surrey) Twickenham (Middlesex)	Richmond-upon-Thames	East Sheen Cemetery (1906) Hampton Cemetery (1859) Mortlake Crematorium (1939)[3] Old Mortlake Cemetery (1887) Richmond Cemetery (1894) South West Middlesex Crematorium (1954)[4] Teddington Cemetery (1879) Twickenham Cemetery (1867)
SW	Kingston-upon-Thames Malden & Coombe Surbiton	Kingston-upon-Thames	Kingston Cemetery (1855) Kingston Crematorium (1952) Surbiton Cemetery (1915)

3. Mortlake Crematorium is jointly owned by Ealing, Hammersmith, Hounslow and Richmond.
4. South West Middlesex Crematorium is jointly owned by Ealing, Hillingdon, Hounslow, Richmond and Spelthorne.

area	pre-1965 authority	present authority	local cemeteries/crematoria
W	Fulham Hammersmith (L.C.C.)	Hammersmith & Fulham	Brompton Cemetery (1840) Fulham Cemetery (1865) Hammersmith Cemetery (1869) Hammersmith New Cemetery (1926) Part of Kensal Green (All Souls) Cemetery (1833) Mortlake Cemetery (1926)[5] Mortlake Crematorium (1939) North Sheen Cemetery (1905) West London Crematorium (1939)
W	St Marylebone Paddington City of Westminster (L.C.C.)	City of Westminster	Paddington New Cemetery, Milespit Hill (1937) Paddington Cemetery, Willesden Lane (1855) St Marylebone Cemetery (1855) St Marylebone Crematorium (1938) Westminster Cemetery (1854) (see Introduction re certain parishes)
W	Chelsea Kensington (L.C.C.) & Chelsea	Royal Borough of Kensington	Gunnersbury Cemetery (1929) Part of Kensal Green (All Souls) Cemetery (1833) Kensington Hanwell Cemetery (1855) Royal Hospital Chelsea Burial Ground (Army; 1692)
W	Acton Ealing Southall (Middlesex)	Ealing	Acton Cemetery (1895) Greenford Park Cemetery (1901) Hanwell Cemetery (1854) Havelock Road Cemetery (1883) Hortus Road Cemetery (1944) Mortlake Crematorium (1939)[6] South Ealing Cemetery (1861) South West Middlesex Crematorium (1954)[7]
W	Brentford & Chiswick Heston & Isleworth (Middlesex)	Hounslow	Bedfont Cemetery (1941) Borough Cemetery (1942) Chiswick New Cemetery (1933) Chiswick Old Cemetery (1888) Feltham Cemetery (1886) Hatton Cemetery (1974) Hounslow Cemetery (1869) Isleworth Cemetery (1880) Mortlake Crematorium (1939)[8] New Brentford Cemetery (1903) South West Middlesex Crematorium (1954)[9]

5. See note 1.
6. See note 1.
7. See note 2.
8. See note 1.
9. See note 2.

area	pre-1965 authority	present authority	local cemeteries/crematoria
W	Hayes & Harlington Ruislip - Northwood Uxbridge Yiewsley & West Drayton (Middlesex)	Hillingdon	Breakspear Crematorium (1958)[10] Cherry Lane Cemetery (1937) Harlington Burial Ground (1871) Harmondsworth Cemetery (1905) Hillingdon & Uxbridge Cemetery (1856) Northwood Cemetery (1915) South West Middlesex Crematorium (1954)[11] Victoria Lane Burial Ground (1871) West Drayton Cemetery (1939)
NW	Hampstead Holborn St Pancras (L.C.C.)	Camden	Hampstead Cemetery (1876) Highgate Cemetery (1839) St Pancras Cemetery (1854)
NW	Wembley Willesden (Middlesex)	Brent	Alperton Cemetery (1917) Carpenders Park Cemetery (1954) Wembley Old Burial Ground (1867) Willesden New Cemetery (1891) Willesden Old Cemetery (1868)
NW	Harrow Middlesex	Harrow	Breakspear Crematorium (1958)[12] Eastcote Lane Cemetery (1922) Harrow Cemetery (1888) Harrow Weald Cemetery (1937) Paines Lane Cemetery (1860s) Pinner New Cemetery (1933) Roxeth Hill Burial Ground (1922) Wealdstone Cemetery (1902)
NW	Barnet East Barnet (Herts) Finchley Friern Barnet Hendon	Barnet	East Finchley Cemetery (1855) Golders Green Crematorium (1903) Great Northern London Cemetery (1861) Hendon Cemetery (1899) Hendon Crematorium (1922) (Middlesex)

MIDDLESEX EXCLUDED FROM GREATER LONDON

	Potters Bar	Hertsmere, Herts.	Allum Lane Lawn Cemetery (1962)

10. Breakspear Crematorium is jointly owned by Harrow and Hillingdon.
11. See note 2.
12. see note 8.

area	pre-1965 authority	present authority	local cemeteries/crematoria
	Staines Sunbury-on-Thames	Spelthorne, Surrey	Ashford Cemetery (1910) South West Middlesex Crematorium (1954) Staines Cemetery (1913) Stanwell Burial Ground (1900) Sunbury Cemetery (1900)

OUTSIDE GREATER LONDON AREA

Brookwood Cemetery, Woking, Surrey (1854)

NON-DENOMINATIONAL CEMETERIES AND CREMATORIA: ALPHABETICAL LISTING

Name & address of cemetery	Location of burial registers	Date registers begin	Can you yourself search
Abney Park Cemetery Stoke Newington High Street,London N16 0LN 020 7275 7557 Search website: http://www.cam.org/ ~hopkde/search.html	Springfield Park Mansion, Springfield, London E5. Microfilm 1840-1978 at Hackney Archives Dept., Rose Lipman Library (Hackney), 43 De Beauvoir Road, London N1 5SQ 020 7241 2886	1840	Yes. Fully searchable online
Acton Cemetery Park Royal Road, The London Borough of Ealing, London W3 6XB	The Cemetery Office, 22/24 Uxbridge Road, London W5 2BP 020 8825 6060	1895	Yes (£38.50 search fee 1999)
All Saints Cemetery	see Nunhead		
All Souls Cemetery	see Kensal Green		
Allum Lane Lawn Cemetery Allum Lane, Borehamwood, Herts. WD6 3PJ 020 8207 7497	Hertsmere Borough Council Civic Offices, Elstree Way, Borehamwood, Herts. WD6 1BR 020 8207 7543	1962	No

Name & address of cemetery	Location of burial registers	Date registers begin	Can you yourself search
Alperton Cemetery Clifford Road, Alperton, Wembley, Middlesex HA0 1AF	Cemeteries Office, Clifford Road, Alperton, Wembley, Middlesex HA0 1AF 020 8902 2385	1917	No
Ashford Cemetery Long Lane, Ashford, Middlesex	Borough of Spelthorne Council Offices, Knowle Green, Staines, Middlesex TW18 1XB 01784 446379	1910	No
Bandon Hill Cemetery Plough Lane, Beddington, Surrey SM6 8JQ	at the Cemetery 020 8647 1024	1899	No
Barkingside Cemetery Longwood Gardens, Barkingside, Ilford, Essex IG5 0ET	Longwood Gardens 020 8708 7560	1923	No
Barkingside Garden of Rest Longwood Gardens, Barkingside, Ilford, Essex IG5 0ET	Longwood Gardens 020 8708 7560	1953	No
Battersea New Cemetery	see Morden Cemetery		
Battersea St Mary's Cemetery	as for Wandsworth Cemetery	1860	No
Beckenham Cemetery Elmers End Road, Beckenham, Kent BR3 4TD	at the Cemetery 020 8650 9290 020 8650 0322	1876	Yes
Beckenham Crematorium Elmers End Road, Beckenham, Kent BR3 4TD	at Beckenham Cemetery 020 8650 9290 020 8650 0322	1956	Yes
Becontree Cemetery	see Eastbrookend Cemetery	1914	Yes

Name & address of cemetery	Location of burial registers	Date registers begin	Can you yourself search
Bedfont Cemetery Bedfont Road, Bedfont, Middlesex TW19	020 8894 2677	1942	Yes
Bexleyheath Cemetery Banks Lane, Broadway, Bexleyheath, Kent DA5	Bexley Local Studies and Archives Centre, Townley Road, Bexleyheath, Kent DA6 7HJ 0208 836 7470 Registers from 1944 at the Cemetery 020 8303 7777 X 3665	1879	Yes; from 1944 No
Biggin Hill Cemetery Kingsmead Avenue, Biggin Hill, Kent TN16 3UB	Cemeteries Section, Department of Leisure Services, Central Library, High Street, Bromley, Kent BR1 1EX 020 8313 4413	1930	Yes
Borough Cemetery Powder Mill Lane, Whitton, Middlesex TW2	as for Bedfont Cemetery	1942	Yes
Breakspear Crematorium Breakspear Road, Ruislip, Middlesex HA4 7SJ	at the Crematorium 01895 556560	1958	Yes
Brockley Cemetery Ladywell Road, London SE13	Lewisham Crematorium and Cemetery Services, Verdant Lane, Catford, London SE6 1TP 020 8698 4955	1858	£20 fee
Bromley Hill Cemetery Bromley Hill, Bromley, Kent BR1 4JU	as for Biggin Hill Cemetery	1907	Yes

Name & address of cemetery	Location of burial registers	Date registers begin	Can you yourself search
Brompton Cemetery Fulham Road, London SW10 9UG	at the Cemetery 020 7352 1201 Friends of Brompton Cemetery South Lodge, Fulham Road 020 7351 9936	1840	No
Brookwood Cemetery Cemetery Pales, Brookwood, Woking, Surrey GU24 OBL 01483 472222	at the Cemetery

Copy registers 1854-1978 at Surrey History Centre, 130 Goldworth Road, Woking GU21 6ND 01483 518737 | 1854 | No |
| **Buckingham Road Cemetery** (formerly known as Great Ilford Cemetery) Buckingham Road, Ilford, Essex IG1 | as Barkingside Cemetery 020 8501 2236 | 1881 | No |
| **Bunhill Fields Burial Ground** City Road, London EC1 | 1713-1854 indexes at The National Archives, Ruskin Avenue, Kew TW9 4DU (RG 4/4652-4657); 1789-1854 interment order books and transcripts of inscriptions (Ms 1092): 18 vols at Guildhall Library, Aldermanbury, London EC2 index at Society of Genealogists Library | | Yes

Yes

Yes |
| **Camberwell New Cemetery** Brenchley Gardens, London SE23 3RD | at the Cemetery 020 7639 3121 | 1927 | Yes |
| **Camberwell Old Cemetery** Forest Hill Road, London SE22 | Camberwell New Cemetery Office, Brenchley Gardens, London SE23 3RD 020 7639 3121 | 1856 | Yes |

Name & address of cemetery	Location of burial registers	Date registers begin	Can you yourself search
Carpenders Park Cemetery Oxhey Lane, Carpenders Park, Nr.Watford, Herts. WD19	as for Alperton Cemetery	1954	No
Chadwell Heath Cemetery Whalebone Lane North, Dagenham, Essex RM6	as for Rippleside Cemetery 020 8270 4740	1907	Yes
Charlton Cemetery Cemetery Lane, London SE7 8DZ	at the Cemetery 020 8856 2232	1864	Yes
Cherry Lane Cemetery Shepiston Lane, Harlington, Middlesex	Cemeteries Department, Civic Centre, High Street, Uxbridge, Middlesex UB8 1UW 01895 250416	1937	No
Chingford Mount Cemetery Old Church Road, London E4 6ST	at the Cemetery 020 8524 5030 Some registers at Waltham Forest Archives, Vestry House Museum, Vestry Road, London E17 9NH 020 8509 1917	1884	No
Chislehurst Cemetery Beaverwood Road, Chislehurst, Kent BR7	as for Biggin Hill Cemetery	1912	Yes
Chiswick New Cemetery Staveley Road, London W4 2SJ 020 8894 2677	part at Cemetery; part at Civic Centre, London Borough of Hounslow, Lampton Road, Hounslow, Middlesex TW3 4DN	1933	Yes
Chiswick Old Cemetery Corney Road, London W4	as for Chiswick New Cemetery	1888	Yes

Name & address of cemetery	Location of burial registers	Date registers begin	Can you yourself search
City of London and Tower Hamlets	see Tower Hamlets Cemetery		
City of London Cemetery Aldersbrook Road, Manor Park, London E12 5DQ 020 8530 2151	original registers 1856-date at Cemetery; copy 1856-1915 at Guildhall Library, Aldermanbury, London EC2P 2EJ (Ms 10,445) 61 vols. Registers of purchased graves 1856-1949 at Corporation of London Record Office, c/o London Metropolitan Archives, 40 Northampton Road, Clerkenwell EC1R 0HB	1856	Yes
City of London Crematorium Aldersbrook Road, Manor Park, London E12 5DQ 020 8530 2151	City of London Cemetery, Aldersbrook Road, Manor Park, London E12 5DQ Registers 1905-43 at Corporation of London Record Office, London Metropolitan Archives, 40 Northampton Road, Clerkenwell EC1R 0HB	1905	Yes
City of Westminster Cemetery	see Hanwell Cemetery		
Crow Lane Cemetery	see Romford Cemetery		
Croydon Cemetery Mitcham Road, Croydon, Surrey CR9 3AT	at the Cemetery 020 8684 3877	1897	Yes
Croydon Crematorium Mitcham Road, Croydon, Surrey CR9 3AT	at Croydon Cemetery 020 8684 3877	1937	Yes
Crystal Palace District Cemetery	see Beckenham Cemetery		

Name & address of cemetery	Location of burial registers	Date registers begin	Can you yourself search
Cuddington Cemetery Lindsey Road, Worcester Park, Sutton, Surrey KT4	Sutton Cemetery, Alcorn Close, Sutton, Surrey SM3 9PX 020 8644 9437	1902	No
Deptford Cemetery	see Brockley Cemetery		
Ealing & Old Brentford Cemetery	see South Ealing Cemetery		
Eastbrookend Cemetery The Chase, off Dagenham Road, Dagenham, Essex RM7	as for Rippleside Cemetery 020 8270 4740	1914	Yes
Eastcote Lane Cemetery Eastcote Lane, South Harrow, Middlesex HA2 8RN	Cemetery Office, Harrow Weald Cemetery, Clamp Hill, Stanmore, Middlesex HA7 3JS 020 8954 1561	1922	No
East Finchley Cemetery (formerly St Marylebone Cemetery), East End Road East Finchley, London N2 9AG	at Hanwell Cemetery 38 Uxbridge Road, London W7 3PP 020 8567 0913 see also Islington & St Pancras Cemeteries	1855	Yes
East London Cemetery Grange Road, Plaistow, London E13 OHB	at the Cemetery 020 7476 5109	1872	Yes
East Sheen Cemetery Sheen Road, Richmond, Surrey TW10 5BJ	London Borough of Richmond Cemeteries Office, East Sheen Cemetery, Sheen Road, Richmond, Surrey TW10 5BJ 020 8876 4511 Search available online Http://www2.richmond.gov.uk/burials/regenq.asp	1906	No

Name & address of cemetery	Location of burial registers	Date registers begin	Can you yourself search
Edmonton Cemetery Church Street, London N9 9HP 020 8360 2157	part at Cemetery; part at Cemetery Department, The Civic Centre, Enfield, Middlesex EN1 3XJ 020 8379 3767	1884	Yes
Elmers End Cemetery	see Beckenham Cemetery		
Eltham Cemetery Rochester Way, London SE9 2RF	as for Charlton Cemetery 020 8856 2232	1935	Yes
Eltham Crematorium Falconwood, Rochester Way Relief Road London SE9 2RF	as for Charlton Cemetery 020 8856 2232	1956	Yes
Enfield Cemetery	see Hertford Road Cemetery & Lavender Hill Cemetery		
Enfield Crematorium Great Cambridge Road, Enfield, Middlesex EN1 4DS	at the Crematorium 020 8363 8324	1938	No; index Yes
Enfield Lawn Cemetery Enfield Crematorium, Great Cambridge Road, Enfield, Middlesex EN1 4DS	Enfield Crematorium 020 8363 8324	1961	Yes
Erith Cemetery Brook Street, Erith, Kent DA8	Registers 1894-1963 at Bexley Local Studies and Archives Centre, Townley Road, Bexleyheath, Kent DA6 7HJ 020 8836 7470 Registers from 1963 at the Cemetery	1894	Yes; from 1963 No
Feltham Cemetery Ashford Road, Feltham, Middlesex TW13	as for Bedfont Cemetery 020 8894 2677	1886	Yes

Name & address of cemetery	Location of burial registers	Date registers begin	Can you yourself search
Forest Park Cemetery and Crematorium Forest Road, Hainault Essex IG6 3HP	at the Cemetery 020 8501 2236	2005	No
Fulham Cemetery Fulham Palace Road, London SW6 3LA	Registers 1865-1960 at London Borough of Hammersmith & Fulham, The Lilla Huset 191 Talgarth Road, London W6 8BJ 020 8741 5159	1865	Yes
Gibraltar Row Burial Ground Bethnal Green E2	at The National Archives, Ruskin Avenue, Kew TW9 4DU (RG 8/305-314); indexed transcript on open shelves	1793-1826	Yes
Golders Green Crematorium Hoop Lane, London NW11 7NL	at the Crematorium 020 8455 2374	1903	No
Great Northern London Cemetery (now New Southgate Cemetery) Brunswick Park Road, London N11 1JJ	at the Cemetery 020 8361 1713	1861	No (£15 since 1933 £25 before, unless date of death known)
Greenford Park Cemetery Windmill Lane, Greenford, Middlesex UB6 9DU	as for Acton Cemetery	1901	Yes (£38.50 search fee)
Greenlawn Memorial Park Chelsham, Warlingham, Surrey CR6 9EQ	Croydon Cemetery, Mitcham Road, Croydon, Surrey CR9 3AT 020 8684 3877	1940	Yes
Greenwich Cemetery Well Hall Road, London SE9 6UA	as for Charlton Cemetery 020 8856 2232	1856	Yes

Name & address of cemetery	Location of burial registers	Date registers begin	Can you yourself search
Greenwich Hospital Burial Ground	see Royal Hospital Cemetery		
Grove Park Cemetery Marvels Lane, Lee, London SE12	Lewisham Crematorium & Cemetery Services, Verdant Lane, Catford, London SE6 1TP 020 8698 4955	1935	£20 fee
Gunnersbury Cemetery Gunnersbury Avenue, London W3 8LE	at the Cemetery 020 8992 2924	1929	No
Hammersmith Cemetery Margravine Road, London W6	Registers 1869-1952 at London Borough of Hammersmith and Fulham Archives, The Lilla Huset, 191 Talgarth Road, London W6 8BJ 020 8741 5159	1869	Yes
Hammersmith New Cemetery Clifford Avenue, London SW14	Registers 1926-52 at London Borough of Hammersmith and Fulham Archives, The Lilla Huset, 191 Talgarth Road, London W6 8BJ 020 8741 5159	1926	Yes
Hampstead Cemetery Fortune Green Road, London NW6 1DR	Closed to new burials 020 8883 1231	1876	No
Hampton Cemetery Hollybush Lane, Hampton, Middlesex TW12 2QS	as for Twickenham Cemetery 020 8876 4511 Search available online http://www2.richmond.gov.uk/burials/regenq.asp	1879	No
Hanwell Cemetery (formerly known as City of Westminster Cemetery and Kensington Cemetery, 31 and 38 Uxbridge Road, London W7 3PP	at the Cemetery 020 8992 2924 (Kensington) 020 8567 0913 (Westminster) Two cemeteries on one site	1854	Yes – phone before

Name & address of cemetery	Location of burial registers	Date registers begin	Can you yourself search
Harlington Burial Ground St Peter's Way, Harlington, Middlesex UB3	as for Cherry Lane Cemetery	1871	No
Harmondsworth Cemetery High Street, Harmondsworth Village, Middlesex UB7	as for Cherry Lane Cemetery	1905	No
Harrow Cemetery Pinner Road, Harrow, Middlesex HA1 4JA	Harrow Weald Cemetery, Clamp Hill, Stanmore, Middlesex HA7 3JS 020 8954 1561	1888	No
Harrow Weald Cemetery Clamp Hill, Stanmore, Middlesex HA7 3JS	at the Cemetery 020 8954 1561	1937	No
Hatton Cemetery Faggs Road, Feltham, Middlesex TW14	as for Bedfont Cemetery 020 8894 2677 Large Moslem section	1974	Yes
Havelock Road Cemetery Church Road, Southall, Middlesex UB2 4NT	as for Acton Cemetery	1883	Yes (£38.50 search fee)
Hendon Cemetery Holders Hill Road, London NW7 1NB	at the Cemetery	1899	Yes
Hendon Crematorium Holders Hill Road, London NW7 1NB	Hendon Cemetery, Holders Hill Road, London NW7 1NB	1922	Yes
Hertford Road Cemetery Hertford Road, Enfield, Middlesex EN3	as for Old Southgate Cemetery	1881	Yes

Name & address of cemetery	Location of burial registers	Date registers begin	Can you yourself search
Highgate Cemetery Swains Lane, London N6 6PJ 020 8340 1834	Camden Local Studies Library, Holborn Library, 32-38 Theobalds Road, London WC1X 8PA 020 7974 6342 Also London Metropolitan Archives 40 Northampton Road, London EC1R 0HB (DL/T/63/1-28) for 1839-71	1839-1984 at Library	Yes – phone before
Hillingdon & Uxbridge Cemetery Hillingdon Hill, Hillingdon, Middlesex UB10	as for Cherry Lane Cemetery	1856	No
Hither Green Cemetery Verdant Lane, Catford, London SE6 1TP	Lewisham Crematorium, Verdant Lane, Catford, London SE6 1TP 020 8698 4955	1873	£20 fee
Honor Oak Crematorium Brenchley Gardens, London SE23 3RD	at the Crematorium 020 7639 3121	1939	Yes
Hornchurch Cemetery Upminster Road, Hornchurch, Essex RM11	Registrar of Cemeteries & Crematoria, South Essex Crematorium, Ockenden Road, Corbets Tey, Upminster, Essex RM14 2UY 01708 222188	1932	No
Hortus Road Cemetery Merrick Road, Southall, Middlesex UB2 4AU	as for Acton Cemetery	1944	Yes (£38.50 search fee)
Hounslow Cemetery Hanworth Road, Hounslow, Middlesex TW4	as for Bedfont Cemetery 020 8894 2677	1869	Yes

Name & address of cemetery	Location of burial registers	Date registers begin	Can you yourself search
Isleworth Cemetery Park Road, Isleworth, Middlesex TW7	as for Bedfont Cemetery 020 8894 2677	1880	Yes
Islington Cemetery High Road, East Finchley, London N2 9AG	at the Cemetery 020 8883 1230/1	1854	Yes
Islington Cemetery **(Trent Park)** Cockfosters Road, Barnet, Herts. EN4	as for Islington Cemetery	1960	Yes
Islington Crematorium High Road, London N2 9AG	as for Islington Cemetery	1937	Yes
Kensal Green (All Souls) **Cemetery** Harrow Road, London W10 4RA	at the Cemetery 020 8969 0152 Also London Metropolitan Archives 40 Northampton Road, London EC1R 0HB (DL/T/41/1-40) for 1833-72 Friends of Kensal Green Cemetery 020 7402 2749	1833	No
Kensington Hanwell **Cemetery** Broadway, London W7	Gunnersbury Cemetery, Gunnersbury Avenue, London W4 020 8992 2924	1855	No
Kingston Cemetery Bonner Hill Road, Kingston-upon-Thames, Surrey KT1 3EZ	at the Cemetery 020 8546 4462	1855	No
Kingston Crematorium Bonner Hill Road, Kingston-upon-Thames, Surrey KT1 3EZ	at the Cemetery & Crematorium Office 020 8546 4462	1952	No

Name & address of cemetery	Location of burial registers	Date registers begin	Can you yourself search
Ladywell Cemetery Ladywell Road, London SE13	Lewisham Cemeteries & Crematorium Services, Verdant Lane, Catford, London SE6 1TP 020 8698 4955	1858	£20 fee
Lambeth Cemetery Blackshaw Road, London SW17 0BY 020 7926 4466	Pre-1929 at Lambeth Archives Department Minet Library, Knatchbull Road. 020 7926 6076 Later registers at the Cemetery Crematorium opened 1955.	1854	Pre-1929 Yes; later No
Lavender Hill Cemetery Cedar Road, Enfield, Middlesex EN2	as for Old Southgate Cemetery	1872	Yes
Lee Cemetery	see Hither Green Cemetery		
Lewisham Cemetery	see Ladywell Cemetery		
Lewisham Crematorium Verdant Lane, Catford, London SE6 1TP	at the Crematorium 020 8698 4955	1956	£20 fee
London Road Cemetery Warner Road, Bromley, Kent BR1	as for Biggin Hill Cemetery	1877	Yes
Manor Park Cemetery Sebert Road, Manor Park, London E7 ONP	at the Cemetery 020 8534 1486	1874	Yes
Manor Park Crematorium Sebert Road, Manor Park, London E7 ONP	at Manor Park Cemetery 020 8534 1486	1955	Yes
Margravine Road Cemetery	see Hammersmith Cemetery		

Name & address of cemetery	Location of burial registers	Date registers begin	Can you yourself search
Merton and Sutton Joint Cemetery Garth Road, Morden, Surrey 020 8337 4420	London Borough of Merton, Recreation Division, 9th Floor, Civic Centre, London Road, Morden, Surrey SM4 5DX 020 8648 4115	1947	No
Mill Hill Cemetery (formerly Paddington New Cemetery) Milespit Hill, London NW7 2RR	at Hanwell Cemetery 020 8567 0913	1937	Yes - phone before
Mitcham Cemetery Church Road, Mitcham, Surrey CR4	as for Merton and Sutton Joint Cemetery	1883	No
Mitcham Cemetery London Road, Mitcham, Surrey CR4 2JB	020 8648 4115	1929	No
Morden Burial Ground South Worple Way and Avenue Gardens, Mortlake, Surrey SW15	see East Sheen Cemetery	1883	No
Morden Cemetery **(Battersea New Cemetery)** Lower Morden Lane, Morden, Surrey SM4 4NU	Putney Vale Cemetery, Stag Lane, London SW15 3DZ 020 8788 2113	1892	No
Mortlake Cemetery Clifford Avenue, London SW14	Registers 1926-52 at London Borough of Hammersmith and Fulham Archives, The Lilla Huset 191 Talgarth Road, London W6 8BJ 020 8741 5159	1926	Yes
Mortlake Crematorium Kew Meadow Path, Richmond, Surrey TW9 4EM	at the Crematorium 020 8876 8056	1939	Yes

Name & address of cemetery	Location of burial registers	Date registers begin	Can you yourself search
New Brentford Cemetery Sutton Lane, Hounslow, Middlesex TW3	as for Bedfont Cemetery 020 8894 2677	1902	Yes
New Southgate Cemetery & Crematorium	see Great Northern London Cemetery		
North East Surrey Crematorium Lower Morden Lane, Morden, Surrey SM4 4NU	at the Crematorium 020 8337 4835	1958	No
North Sheen Cemetery Lower Richmond Road, London SW14	Registers 1909-64 at London Borough of Hammersmith and Fulham Archives, The Lilla Huset, 191 Talgarth Road, London W6 8BJ 020 8741 5159	1905	Yes
Northwood Cemetery Chestnut Avenue, Northwood, Middlesex HA6	as for Cherry Lane Cemetery	1915	No
Norwood Cemetery	see West Norwood Cemetery		
Nunhead Cemetery Linden Grove, London SE15	as for Camberwell New Cemetery Also London Metropolitan Archives 40 Northampton Road, EC1R 0HB (DW/T/515-539) for 1842-71 Friends of Nunhead Cemetery http://www.queries.demon.co.uk/fonc/	1840	Yes
Oldchurch Cemetery	see Romford Cemetery		
Old Mortlake Cemetery South Worple Way, London SW14 8BP	Search available online http://www2.richmond.gov.uk/burials/regenq.asp	1887	No
Old Southgate Cemetery Waterfall Road, London N14 7JS	Cemetery Department, The Civic Centre, Enfield, Middlesex 020 8379 3767	c.1880	Yes

Name & address of cemetery	Location of burial registers	Date registers begin	Can you yourself search
Paddington New Cemetery	see Mill Hill Cemetery		
Paddington Old Cemetery Willesden Lane, London NW6 7SD	as for Alperton Cemetery	1855	No
Paines Lane Cemetery Paines Lane, Pinner, Middlesex HA5 5BP	London Borough of Harrow Cemetery Office, Harrow Weald Cemetery, Clamp Hill, Stanmore, Middlesex HA7 3JS 020 8954 1561	1860s	Yes
Pinner New Cemetery Pinner Road, Pinner, Middlesex HA2	as for Paines Lane Cemetery	1933	No
Plaistow Cemetery Burnt Ash Lane, Bromley, Kent BR1	as for Biggin Hill Cemetery	1892	Yes - phone before
Plumstead Cemetery Wickham Lane, London SE2 0NS	as for Charlton Cemetery 020 8856 2232	1890	Yes
Putney Lower Common Cemetery Mill Hill Road, London SW13	Putney Vale Cemetery, Stag Lane, Putney, London SW15 3DZ 020 8788 2113	1855	No
Putney Vale Cemetery Stag Lane, Putney, London SW15 3DZ	at the Cemetery 020 8788 2113	1891	No
Queen's Road Cemetery Queen's Road, Croydon, Surrey CR0 2PR	Croydon Cemetery, Mitcham Road, Croydon, Surrey CR9 3AT 020 8684 3877	1861	Yes

Name & address of cemetery	Location of burial registers	Date registers begin	Can you yourself search
Rainham Cemetery Upminster Road North, Rainham, Essex RM13	as for Hornchurch Cemetery	1902	No
Richmond Cemetery Lower Grove Road, Richmond-upon-Thames, Surrey TW10 6HP	Cemeteries Office, East Sheen Cemetery, Sheen Road, Richmond, Surrey TW10 8BJ Search available online Http://www2.richmond.gov.uk/burials/regenq.asp	1839	No
Rippleside Cemetery Ripple Road, Barking, Essex IG11 9PF	at the Cemetery 020 8270 4740	1886	Yes
Roding Lane Cemetery Roding Lane North, South Woodford, London E18	Barkingside Cemetery, Longwood Gardens, Barkingside, Ilford, Essex 020 8708 7560	1940	No
Romford Cemetery Dagenham Road, Romford, Essex RM7	as for Hornchurch Cemetery. Duplicate set of registers 1888-1953 at Information Services, St Edward's Way, Romford, Essex 01708 432393/4 Index to Registers 1871-1953 Published by East of London FHS	1871	No
Roxeth Hill Burial Ground Roxeth Hill, Harrow, Middlesex HA2 0JM	Harrow Weald Cemetery, Clamp Hill, Stanmore, Middlesex HA7 3JS 020 8954 1561	1922	No
Royal Hospital Cemetery (Navy) East Greenwich SE10 9LW	The National Archives, Ruskin Avenue, Kew TW9 4DU (RG 8/16-18)	1848-64	Yes
Royal Hospital Chelsea Burial Ground (Army) Royal Hospital Road, London SW3	The National Archives, Ruskin Avenue, Kew TW9 4DU (RG 4/4330-32, 4387)	1692-1856	Yes

Name & address of cemetery	Location of burial registers	Date registers begin	Can you yourself search
St Luke's Cemetery Magpie Hall Lane, Bromley, Kent BR2 9PD	as for Biggin Hill Cemetery	1894	Yes - phone before
St Mary Cray Cemetery Star Lane, St Mary Cray, Orpington, Kent BR5	as for Biggin Hill Cemetery	1881	Yes - phone before
St Marylebone Cemetery	see East Finchley Cemetery		
St Marylebone Crematorium East End Road, East Finchley, London N2 0RZ	at the Crematorium 020 8343 2233	1938	No
St Pancras Cemetery High Road, East Finchley, London N2 9AG	at the Cemetery 020 8883 1231	1854	Yes
St Thomas Square Cemetery Mare Street, Hackney, London E8	The National Archives, Ruskin Avenue, Kew TW9 4DU (RG 8/41)	1837-76	Yes
Sidcup Cemetery Foots Cray Lane, Sidcup, Kent DA14	Registers 1912-63 at Bexley Local Studies and Archives Centre, Townley Road, Bexleyheath, Kent DA6 7HJ 0208 836 7470	1912	Yes to 1963
South Ealing Cemetery South Ealing Road, Ealing, London W5 4QP	as for Acton Cemetery	1861	Yes (£38.50 search fee)
South Essex Crematorium Ockenden Road, Corbets Tey, Upminster, Essex RM14 2UY	at the Crematorium 01708 222188	1950	No
Southgate Cemetery	see Old Southgate Cemetery		

Name & address of cemetery	Location of burial registers	Date registers begin	Can you yourself search
South London Crematorium Rowan Road, London SW16 5JG	Streatham Park Cemetery, Rowan Road, London SW16 5JG 020 8679 4164	1936	No
South Metropolitan Cemetery	see West Norwood Cemetery		
South West Middlesex Crematorium, Hounslow Road, Hanworth, Feltham, Middlesex TW13 5JH	at the Crematorium 020 8894 9001	1954	No
Spa Fields Cemetery Clerkenwell EC1	The National Archives Ruskin Avenue, Kew TW9 4DU Index at Society of Genealogists (RG 4/4316-22, 4366-67)	1778-1849	Yes
Staines Cemetery London Road, Staines, Middlesex TW18 4JQ 01784 452930	Borough of Spelthorne Council Offices, Knowle Green, Staines, Middlesex TW18 1XB 01784 452930	1913	No
Stanwell Burial Ground Town Lane, Stanwell, Staines, Middlesex TW19	as for Ashford Cemetery	1900	No
Streatham Cemetery Garratt Lane, London SW17 OLT	at the Cemetery 020 7926 4466	1893	No
Streatham Park Cemetery Rowan Road, London SW16 5JG	at the Cemetery 020 8679 4164	1911	No
Sunbury Cemetery Green Way, Sunbury, Middlesex TW16 6NW 01932 780244	as for Ashford Cemetery	1900	No

Name & address of cemetery	Location of burial registers	Date registers begin	Can you yourself search
Surbiton Cemetery Lower Marsh Lane, Kingston-upon-Thames, Surrey KT1 3BN	Kingston Cemetery, Bonner Hill Road, Kingston-upon-Thames, Surrey KT1 3EZ 020 8546 4463	1915	No
Sutton Cemetery Alcorn Close, Sutton, Surrey SM3 9PX	at the Cemetery 020 8644 9437	1889	No
Teddington Cemetery Shacklegate Lane, Teddington TW11 8SF	Search available online http://www2.richmond.gov.uk/burials/regenq.asp	1879	No
Tottenham Cemetery White Hart Lane, Tottenham, London N17	Enfield Crematorium, Great Cambridge Road, Enfield, Middlesex EN1 4DS 020 8363 8324	1856	Yes
Tottenham Park Cemetery Montagu Road, London NW4 3ER	at the Cemetery 020 8807 1617	1912	Yes
Tottenham & Wood Green Crematorium	see Enfield Crematorium		
Tower Hamlets Cemetery Southern Grove, London E3	London Metropolitan Archives, 40 Northampton Road, London EC1R 0HB 1841-1966 (CTHC/1/1-42) 1841-52 Indexed transcript at Society of Genealogists	1841	Yes
Trent Park Cemetery	see Islington Cemetery, Cockfosters Road		
Twickenham Cemetery Hospital Bridge Road, Twickenham, Middlesex TW2 6LD	Cemeteries Office, East Sheen Cemetery, Sheen Road, Richmond, Surrey TW10 SBJ Search available online Http://www2.richmond.gov.uk/burials/regenq.asp	1868	No

Name & address of cemetery	Location of burial registers	Date registers begin	Can you yourself search
Upminster Cemetery Ockenden Road, Corbets Tey, Upminster, Essex RMl4 2UY	as for Hornchurch Cemetery	1902	No
Uxbridge Cemetery	see Hillingdon & Uxbridge Cemetery		
Victoria Lane Burial Ground Victoria Lane, Harlington, Middlesex UB3	as for Cherry Lane Cemetery	1871	No
Victoria Park Cemetery Hackney, London E3	The National Archives, Ruskin Avenue, Kew TW9 4DU (RG 8/42-51)	1853-76	Yes
Walthamstow Cemetery Queen's Road, London E17 8QP 020 8524 5030	Chingford Mount Cemetery, Old Church Road, London E4 6ST 020 8524 5030	1872	No
Wandsworth Cemetery Magdalen Road, London SW18 3NP	Central Cemeteries Office, Putney Vale Cemetery, Stag Lane, Putney, London SW15 3DZ 020 8788 2113	1878	No
Wealdstone Cemetery Byron Road, Wealdstone, Harrow, Middlesex HA3	as for Harrow Weald Cemetery	1902	No
Wembley Old Burial Ground High Road, Wembley, Middlesex HA0	as for Alperton Cemetery	1867	Yes - phone before
West Drayton Cemetery Harmondsworth Road, West Drayton, Middlesex UB7	as for Cherry Lane Cemetery	1939	No

Name & address of cemetery	Location of burial registers	Date registers begin	Can you yourself search
West Ham Cemetery Cemetery Road, Forest Gate, London E7 9DG	at the Cemetery 020 8534 1566	1854	Yes
West London and Westminster Cemetery	see Brompton Cemetery		
West London Cemetery	see West Norwood Cemetery		
West London Crematorium Harrow Road, London W10 4RA	as for Kensal Green Cemetery	1939	No
Westminster Cemetery (City of)	see Hanwell Cemetery		
West Norwood Cemetery Norwood Road, London SE27 9JU	at the Cemetery 020 7926 7900 Also London Metropolitan Archives 40 Northampton Road, London EC1R 0HB (DW/T/899-969) for 1838-1918 Friends http://www.fownc.org/	1837	No
West Norwood Crematorium Norwood Road, London SE27 9JU	West Norwood Cemetery, Norwood Road, London SE27 9JU	1915	No
Whitton Cemetery	local name for Twickenham Cemetery		
Willesden Lane Cemetery	see Paddington Cemetery		
Willesden New Cemetery Franklyn Road, London NW10 9TE 020 8902 2385	as for Alperton Cemetery	1891	Yes
Willesden Old Cemetery Neasden Lane, London NW1	as for Alperton Cemetery	1868	Yes – phone before

Name & address of cemetery	Location of burial registers	Date registers begin	Can you yourself search
Wimbledon Cemetery Gap Road, London SW19	as for Morden & Sutton Joint Cemetery	1876	No
Woodgrange Park Cemetery 540 Romford Road, London E7 8AF	1889-1981 at Badgehurst Ltd., Fen Lane, Orsett, Grays, Essex RM16 3LT 020 8472 3433	1889	No
Woodgreen Cemetery Wolves Lane, Wood Green N22	020 8363 8324	1996	
Woolwich Cemeteries Kings Highway & Camdale Road, London SE18 2DS	as for Charlton Cemetery 020 8856 2232	1856 & 1885	Yes

RESTRICTED CEMETERIES AND CREMATORIA

ARMY **Royal Hospital Chelsea Burial Ground** London SW3	The National Archives, Ruskin Avenue, Kew TW9 4DU (RG 4/4330-32, 4387)	1692- 1856	Yes
NAVY **Royal Hospital Cemetery** East Greenwich SE10 9LW	The National Archives, Ruskin Avenue, Kew TW9 4DU (RG 8/16-18)	1848-64	Yes
ROMAN CATHOLIC **Mortlake Catholic Cemetery** North Worple Way, London SW14	St Mary Magdalen, North Worple Way, London SW14 Search available online http://www2.richmond.gov.uk/burials/regenq.asp	1852	Yes
St Mary's Cemetery Kensal Green, Harrow Road, London NW10 5NU	at the Cemetery 020 8969 1145 Copy, 1858-76, Catholic Family History Society	1858	No

Name & address of cemetery	Location of burial registers	Date registers begin	Can you yourself search
St Patrick's Leytonstone Cemetery Langthorne Road, London E11 4HL	at the Cemetery 020 8539 2451 Copy, 1861-70, & index, 1861-80, Catholic Family History Society	1861	Yes
South London Crematorium, Rowan Road London SW16	although separated into its own physical area there are no separate registers - see above lists for details	1936	No

JEWISH

The reviser is most grateful to Charles Tucker, who supplied the information for this section.

Some important general considerations apply to this population group where the organisation is a more important factor than the residential location of the deceased. Although there are clear divisions between the adherents of the various traditional and modernist movements, unaffiliated Jews (a large proportion of the community) can apply to any institution. Whether they are interred often depends in the last instance on their next of kin or legal representatives providing satisfactory proof of their religious status and a willingness to pay the requisite fees. The burials of indigents has always been the legal responsibility of the United Synagogue.

Cremation is not a practice sanctioned by the Orthodox, but is permitted by the other religious bodies. Ashes can be interred, placed in a columbarium, or otherwise disposed of. Golders Green Crematorium, being near a major centre of Jewish population, is the one most frequently resorted to.

Due to current security problems, neither staff at head offices or in the cemeteries can routinely deal with visitors requiring extended searches. The cemetery staff may be more accommodating where an approximate date is known, otherwise, one has to write in. Whether or not a fee is charged depends in many cases on the nature of the enquiry. Unauthorised photography is not permitted on some sites.

ORTHODOX: ASHKENAZI

United Synagogue (created by act of Parliament, 1870)

(United Synagogue) Burial Society:
Finchley Office, (Bushey and Willesden Cemeteries),
Ground Floor, Finchley Synagogue,
Kinloss Gardens, Finchley, London, N3 3DU.
020 8343 3456.
Burial authorisations from 1974. All burial entries computerised from 1858.

Ilford Office, (West Ham, Plashet and East Ham Cemeteries),
Schaller House, Ilford Synagogue,
28 Beehive Lane, Ilford, Essex, IG1 3RT.
Burial authorisations from 1994. All burial entries computerised from 1858.

United Synagogue Archives
735 High Road, North Finchley, NW12 0US
Burial authorisation registers 1872-1973 (slightly incomplete ante 1905, due to wartime bombing). General burial registers 1872-1912.

This repository also possesses general burial registers, deposited by the following original Constituent Synagogues. No grave sites are listed in these volumes.

Great Synagogue 1791-1872

Hambro Synagogue 1797-1872

New Synagogue 1812-1872

The registers of the Great and Hambro Synagogues were microfilmed by the Mormons 1946-47 and can be viewed via their family history centres worldwide.

Current cemeteries
(by date of opening)

West Ham Cemetery,
Buckingham Road, Forest Lane, London E15
Opened 1858. Closed 2002. Register from 1905 at Superintendent's Office, Waltham Abbey Cemetery. The following are deposited in the United Synagogue Archives:

New Synagogue Section 1858-71
Great Synagogue 1858-72. This volume became a General Register from 1871-1889. Registers in United Synagogue Archives.

Willesden Cemetery,
Beaconsfield Road, London NW10 2JE
Opened 1873. Registers at Cemetery office.

Plashet Cemetery,
High Street North, London E12
Opened 1896. Records at the Ilford Burial Society office.

East Ham Cemetery,
Marlow Road, High Street South, London E6 3QG
020 8472 0554 or 020 8518 2868
Opened 1919. Records at the Ilford Burial Society office.

Bushey Cemetery,
Little Bushey Lane, Bushey, Hertfordshire WD23
020 8950 6299 or 020 8343 3456
Opened 1947. Registers at Cemetery office.

Waltham Abbey Cemetery,
Skillet Hill (Honey Lane), Waltham Abbey, Essex EN9
01992 714492 or 020 8518 2868
Opened 1961. Registers at Cemetery office.

Disused Burial Grounds maintained by the United Synagogue
(by date of opening)

Alderney Road Cemetery
Alderney Road, London E1
Purchased 1696.

Extended 1749 by purchase of site described as being situated in Three Colt Yard, Mile End, Hamlet of Mile End Old Town, Stepney. Belonged to the Great Synagogue. Closed for burials 1852. The oldest Ashkenazi Cemetery in the United Kingdom. Transcripts of all legible inscriptions, together with a plan were published in Bernard Susser, *Alderney Road Jewish Cemetery, London, E1 1697-1853* (The United Synagogue in association with The Working Party on Jewish Monuments in the U. K. and Ireland, 1997.)

Hoxton Cemetery   as Alderney Road Cemetery
Hoxton Street, Hoxton Old Town, London N1
Purchased 1707, last burial 1878. Belonged to the Hambro Synagogue. Remains exhumed and reinterred in West Ham Cemetery, 1961. Transcript of 35 legible portions of Hebrew inscriptions plus translation into English made by Dayan Mendlesohn during 1927/1928 have been entered into the United Synagogue's computerised index.

Brady Street Cemetery,
Brady Street, London E1
Purchased 1761, extended 1795, closed for burials 1858. Originally known as Ducking Pond Lane, Bethnal Green and North Street, Whitechapel. Part belonged to the Great Synagogue and a portion to the New Synagogue. Burial Registers for Privileged Members 1796-1858 and Strangers 1796-1858 interred by the Great Synagogue, plus two separate index books in the possession of the United Synagogue Archives.

Hackney Cemetery,
Lauriston Road, London E9
Purchased 1788, Cemetery closed by Order in Council 1886. Formerly known as Grove Street, Hackney, and belonged to the Hambro Synagogue. Burial registers 1788-1813, 1863-70 are in the United Synagogue Archives.

Federation of Synagogues (established 1887)

Sexton's office,
Federation of Synagogues Burial Society,
65 Watford Way, Hendon,
London NW4 3AQ
020 8202 3903
General burial registers from 1890.

Edmonton Cemetery,
Montague Road, Angel Road,
Lower Edmonton,
London N18 2NF
020 8807 2268
Opened 1890, closed for burials save in reserved graves, 1989. Registers in Cemetery office.

Rainham Cemetery,
Upminster Road North,
Rainham, Essex
01708 552825
Opened 1938. Registers in Cemetery office.

Union of Orthodox Hebrew Congregations (Founded 1926)

Adath Yisroel Burial Society,
Carterhatch Lane,
Enfield EN1 4BG
020 8363 3384
All enquires should initially be addressed to the Sexton's office at this address. All burial entries are computerised

Enfield Cemetery,
Carterhatch Lane,
Enfield EN1 4BG
020 8363 3384
Opened 1926. Records believed to be at Cemetery.

Silver Street Cemetery,
Cheshunt,
Hertfordshire EN7
020 8802 6262
Members of the Adath Yisroel Community who died before the establishment of the Carterhatch Lane Cemetery were buried in a separate section of the Western Synagogue's ground at Montagu Road, Edmonton.

The Assembly of Masorti Synagogues (Established 1985)
1097 Finchley Road,
London NW11 0PU
020 8201 8772
Funerals are dealt with by the Western Marble Arch Synagogue and the Jewish Joint Burial Society.

Independent Orthodox Congregations

Western Synagogue
The Western Marble Arch Synagogue (est. 1991, is the successor to the Western Synagogue (est. 1761 and the Marble Arch Synagogue. Burial Society:
32 Great Cumberland Place,
London, W1H 7DJ.
020 7723 9333.
Registers 1874+

Bullscross Ride Cemetery,
Bullscross Ride,
Cheshunt, Hertfordshire
EN7 5HT
01992 717820
Records 1968+ in Cemetery office

Queen's Elm Parade,
Fulham Road,
London SW3
Opened 1815, closed save for reserved graves 1884. The registers and allied records 1815-1881 listed by Cecil Roth, *Records of the Western Synagogue* (1932) and Arthur Barnett, *The Western Synagogue through Two Centuries (1761-1961)*, (1962) were destroyed by enemy action.

West End Great Synagogue
Chesed V"Ameth Burial Society is now part of the Western Charitable Foundation (2005) located at The Western Marble Arch Synagogue.
32 Great Cumberland Place,
London W1H 7DS.
020 7724 8121
General registers from 1915.

Rowan Road Cemetery,
Greyhound Lane,
Streatham,
London SW16
020 8764 1566
Opened 1915. Records in Cemetery office.

Bullscross Ride Cemetery,
Bullscross Ride,
Cheshunt, Hertfordshire
EN7 5HT
Details as under Western Marble Arch Synagogue. Records in Cemetery office.

Maiden Lane Synagogue,
Westminster WC2

Bancroft Road Cemetery,
Bancroft Road,
London E1
In use c.1810-1920. Registers 1875-1903 listed in Cecil Roth, *Records of the Western Synagogue* (1932) and Arthur Barnett, *The Western Synagogue through Two Centuries (1761-1961)*, (1962) were destroyed in the bombing of the Western Synagogue, 1941. From 1895-1907 this now defunct Synagogue owned a strip of land subsequently incorporated into the Federation of Synagogues Cemetery at Edmonton. Register 1895-1907 remains in the custody of the Western Marble Arch Synagogue.

ORTHODOX: SEPHARDI

Spanish and Portuguese Jews Congregation

Burial Society,
Communal Offices,
2 Ashworth Road,
London W9 1JY
020 7289 2573

General registers from 1897.

Current Cemeteries
(by date of opening)

Hoop Lane Cemetery,
Golders Green,
London NW11
020 8455 2569 Opened 1897. Registers in Cemetery office.

Edgwarebury Cemetery,
Edgwarebury Lane, Edgware,
Middlesex HA8 8QP
020 8958 3388 Opened 1968. Registers in Cemetery office.

Disused Burial Grounds

Velho Cemetery,
253 Mile End Road,
London E1
Opened 1657 - the oldest Jewish Burial Ground in the United Kingdom. Transcript of entries in register 1657-1742 printed by Richard D. Barnett as "The Burial Register of the Spanish and Portuguese Jews, London, 1657-1753" (with some later entries) in *Miscellanies of the Jewish Historical Society of England, volume 6* (1962).

Nuevo Cemetery,
329 Mile End Road,
London E1
Opened 1733, those buried up to 1874 were reinterred without individual identification in Dytchleys, Coxtie Green, Brentwood, Essex in 1973. Transcript of Register, 1733-1918, plus legible Monumental Inscriptions published as *Bevis Marks Records VI*, 1997

REFORM

West London Synagogue (of British Jews, organised 1840),
Sexton's Office,
33 Seymour Place,
London W1
020 8455 2569
General Registers from 1897 in Office.

Hoop Lane Cemetery,
Golders Green,
London NW 11
020 8455 2569
Opened 1897. Registers in Cemetery office.

Edgwarebury Cemetery,
Edgwarebury Lane,
Edgware,
Middlesex HA8 8LW
020 8958 3388
Opened 1968. Registers in Cemetery office.

Disused Burial Ground:

Kingsbury Road,
Balls Pond Road,
London N1
Register 1844-1951 in archives at West London Synagogue of British Jews.

Jewish Joint Burial Society (Est. 1968)
Alyth Gardens,
Finchley Road,
London NW11
020 8455 8579
Registers from 1968 at Society's Office.

Bullscross Ride Cemetery,
Bullscross Ride,
Cheshunt,
Hertfordshire EN7 5HT
Details as under Western Marble Arch Synagogue.

The Hendon Reform Synagogue runs its own Cemetery which is situated in the
Great Northern London Cemetery,
Brunswick Park Road,
London N11 1JJ
Opened 1968. The records are kept at the Synagogue, Danescroft Gardens, London NW4 2NA.
020 8361 1713

North West Surrey Reform Synagogue,
Horvath Close,
Rosslyn Park,
Oatlands Drive,
Weybridge,
Surrey KT13 9QZ
utilises a Jewish section in Elmbridge Borough Council Municipal Cemetery, Brooklands Lane,
Weybridge. The separate Jewish section contains areas both for interments and the burial of
cremated remains c.1970 to date. Registers held at the Borough Engineers and Surveyors
Department, Elmbridge Borough Council, 1 High Street, Esher, Surrey KT10 9RR. Open 8.45am
- 4.15pm Monday to Friday. 01932 228844. The Cemetery Office only possesses basic lists.

LIBERAL

Union of Liberal and Progressive Synagogues,
The Montagu Centre,
21 Maple Street,
London W1T 4BE
020 7580 1663

Edgwarebury Cemetery,
Edgwarebury Lane,
Middlesex HA8 8LW
020 7958 3388
Opened 1968. Registers in Cemetery office (Details as for West London Synagogue).

Duplicate set of records at Union of Liberal and Progressive Synagogues office and at the
Cemetery. Until mid-1990 the undertaker used only supplied details of burials (and burial of
cremated remains) of those actually interred at the Edgwarebury Cemetery to the Society. After
this date the undertaker supplied such details for all, including those whose ashes are disposed of
elsewhere. Before 1976, burials and cremations performed under the auspices of the Liberal
Jewish Synagogue. The following congregations participate: Barkingside Progressive, Belsize
Square Synagogue, Chiltern Progressive, Ealing Liberal, Finchley Progressive, Harrow and
Wembley Progressive, North London Progressive, Northwood and Pinner Liberal, Southgate
Progressive, West Central Liberal, Woodford and District Liberal.

Liberal Jewish Cemetery
Pound Lane,
Harlesden Road,
London NW10 2HG
020 8459 1635 Opened 1914. The cemetery of the Liberal Jewish Synagogue, St John's Wood.

Established 1910 by the Jewish Religious Union.

South London Liberal Synagogue,
Prentis Road,
London SW16 1QB
020 8769 4787

Section in Streatham Park Cemetery,
Rowan Road,
London SW16
Full records held at the Cemetery. The section is leased from the local authority. Details of burials and reserved graves are held at the Synagogue office

St George's Settlement Synagogue (defunct)
A constituent of the Reform Synagogues of Great Britain and the Union of Liberal and Progressive Synagogues. Funerals were dealt with by the Western Marble Arch Synagogue and the Jewish Joint Burial Society.

Kingston Liberal Synagogue,
Rushett Road,
Long Ditton,
Surrey KT7 OUX
(020 8398 7400) formerly shared a section of the municipal cemetery at Weybridge run under the auspices of Elmbridge District Council. From late 1990 they have used a consecrated section in Long Ditton Cemetery, Rectory Lane. Both Weybridge and Long Ditton Cemeteries are for Elmbridge Jews regardless of affiliation.

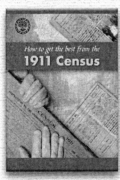